JOSEPH HAYDN

SYMPHONY No. 49

F minor / f-Moll / Fa mineur
Hob. I: 49
"La Passione"

Edited by / Herausgegeben von
H. C. Robbins Landon

Ernst Eulenburg Ltd

London · Mainz · Madrid · New York · Paris · Tokyo · Toronto · Zürich

Haydn, Symphony No. 49, F minor,
" La Passione " *

Haydn, Symphonie No. 49, F moll,
" La Passione " *

For this edition, Haydn's autograph, in the Royal Swedish Academy of Music, Stockholm, has again been compared to the excellent score in the B. & H. Gesamtausgabe, Series I, Vol. 4, edited by Helmut Schultz in 1933. In addition, some old MS. sources in the Gesellschaft der Musikfreunde, Vienna, were consulted, as well as the set of parts in the Esterházy Archives, now National Library, Budapest.

Source A. Autograph, Royal Swedish Academy of Music, Stockholm. 4to, 24 pages on 14-stave paper from the Esterházy paper mill at Lockenhaus (watermarks: springing stag with letters " IGS "). Title of the 1st page, in Haydn's handwriting: " Sinfonia in F minore "; at the head of the 2nd page (1st page of music): " In Nomine Domini. [right:] del giuseppe Haydn / 768." The instruments read: " 2 Corni in F / Oboe 1ma /⫙ Oboe 2da / Violino 1mo /[Violino]/2do / Viola / Basso ". At the end of the MS.: " Fine. Laus Deo ".

Source B. MS. parts in the Esterházy Archives, now National Library, Budapest. The 1st and 2nd violin parts and the " Basso " are in two copies, the other parts single. The title page notes that the symphony was " in Dupplo ", i.e. in two copies, and there is reason to believe that the present parts were not corrected, if indeed they were used at the first performance under Haydn's direction (which seems unlikely). The MS. contains many mistakes and inaccuracies.

Source C. MS. parts, Gesellschaft der Musikfreunde, Vienna, cat. XIII, 6655; the title page reads: " No. 64. 26 Bögen. nel suo antisiasmo [sic] il Quakero di bel' humore. / questa Sinfonia serve di compagna à quelle / del Philosopho Inglese del istesso autore. / In F minore / Sinfonia / a / 2 Violini / 2: Oboe / 2: Corni / Viola / con / Basso / Del Sigre Giuseppe Hayden [sic] / [theme] / Manguccide Rossi mpria." 4to paper of 10 staves.

Source D. MS. parts, same library and same cat. no. Title page reads: " In F♭ / Sinfonia /

Für diese Ausgabe wurde nochmals Haydns Autograph, das sich in der Bibliothek der Königlich Schwedischen Musikalischen Akademie (Stockholm) befindet, mit der von Helmut Schultz 1933 sorgfältigst vorbereiteten Partitur der B. & H. Gesamtausgabe, Serie I, Band 4, verglichen. Zusätzlich wurden noch einige alte MS-Quellen der Gesellschaft der Musikfreunde, Wien, und die MS-Stimmen des Esterházy-Archives (jetzt Nationalbibliothek Budapest) herangezogen.

Quelle A. Autograph, Bibliothek der Königlich Schwedischen Musikalischen Akademie, Stockholm. Hochformat, 24 Seiten, 14-zeiliges Papier aus der Esterházischen Papiermühle zu Lockenhaus (Wasserzeichen: Springender Hirsch mit den Buchstaben "IGS"). Titel auf der ersten Seite in Haydns Handschrift: "Sinfonia in F minore"; Kopftitel auf der zweiten Seite: "In Nomine Domini. [rechts] [del giuseppe Haydn / 768." Stimmen: " 2 Corni in F / Oboe 1ma / Oboe 2da / Violino 1 mo / [Violino] 2do / Viola / Basso". Am Schluss der Partitur: "Fine. Laus Deo."

Quelle B. MS-Stimmen, Esterházy-Archiv, jetzt Nationalbibliothek Budapest. Violine I, II und " Basso " sind in Duplikatstimmen, die übrigen nur einfach vorhanden. Die Titelseite notiert, dass die Symphonie " in Dupplo ", das heisst in zwei Kopien vorläge, und man könnte annehmen, dass diese Stimmen, falls sie überhaupt bei der ersten Aufführung unter Haydns Leitung verwendet wurden (was unwahrscheinlich ist), nicht korrigiert sind. Das MS weist viele Fehler und Flüchtigkeiten auf.

Quelle C. MS-Stimmen, Gesellschaft der Musikfreunde, Wien, Kat.: XIII, 6655; Titel: " No. 64. 26 Bögen. nel suo antisiasmo [sic] il Quakero di bel' humore. / questa Sinfonia serve di compagna à quelle / del Philosopho Inglese del istesso autore. / In F minore / Sinfonia / a / 2 Violini / 2: Oboe / 2: Corni /

---

* The origin of the title is not known to us: it appears early in the 19th century. *La Passione* obviously refers to the sombre character of the symphony, and especially the *Adagio.*

* Der Ursprung dieses Titels ist uns nicht bekannt: er erscheint erstmalig im frühen 19. Jahrhundert. "La Passione" bezieht sich augenscheinlich auf den düsteren Charakter der Symphonie und besonders den des "Adagio."

a / 2 Violini / 2 oboe / 2 corni / Viola e Basso / Del Sig Giuseppe Haydn." From the Kees Collection. Several duplicate string parts in another handwriting, probably added considerably later. The original parts on 4to paper, probably from a German paper mill (watermarks: number " 4 " over a heart containing illegible letters); there are 12 staves per page.

Source E. MS. parts, same library and same cat. no. Title page reads: " CCXCVI / In F minore / Sinfonia / a / 2: Violini / 2: Oboe / 2: Corni / Viola / Con / Basso [theme] / Del Sigre Giuseppe Haydn." Written by a professional Viennese copyist on Italian paper (watermarks: three half-moons and letters " AS " under cartouche); 4to paper of 10 staves.

The following alterations were introduced into the definitive score of the Gesamtausgabe:

General

(1) The presence of a harpsichord* (*cembalo*), though not specifically required in Haydn's score, was a matter of course in the 18th century, and a performance of the work without this instrument is unthinkable. Particularly in the 1st movt. (e.g. bars 39ff), the harpsichord fulfils a necessary harmonic, as well as colouristic, function.

(2) The bassoon, also not specifically required by Haydn, was part of the 18th century thorough-bass tradition. Examination of Haydn's early symphonies shows that he, too, assumed that a bassoon would always be used as part of the *basso continuo*; for there are many works in which he suddenly writes " Fagotto Solo " in the bass stave, without having mentioned the instrument at the beginning of the movement. Such passages occur *inter alia* in Symphony No. 40 (autograph in the British Museum), in No. 42 (autograph in the Esterházy Archives), in No. 45 (autograph in the Esterházy Archives) and in No. 55 (autograph in Berlin

Viola / con / Basso / Del Sigre Giuseppe Hayden [sic] / [Thema] / Manguccide Rossi mpria." Hochformat, 10-zeiliges Papier.

Quelle D. MS-Stimmen aus derselben Bibliothek und unter der gleichen Katalognummer. Titel: " In F♭ / Sinfonia / a / 2 Violini / 2 oboe / 2 corni / Viola e Basso / Del Sig Giuseppe Haydn." Zur Kees-Sammlung gehörend. Mehrere duplikate Streicherstimmen in anderer Handschrift, wahrscheinlich wesentlich später. Das Papier der Originalstimmen in Hochformat, 12-zeilig, dürfte aus einer deutschen Papiermühle stammen (Wasserzeichen: Zahl " 4 " über einem Herz mit unleserlichen Buchstaben).

Quelle E. MS-Stimmen aus derselben Bibliothek und unter der gleichen Katalognummer. Titel: " CCXCVI. / In F minore / Sinfonia / a / 2: Violini / 2: Oboe / 2: Corni / Viola / Con / Basso [Thema] / Del Sigre Giuseppe Haydn." Von einem Wiener Berufskopisten auf italienischem Papier geschrieben (Wasserzeichen: drei Halbmonde und Buchstaben " AS " unter Kartusche); Hochformat, 10-zeiliges Papier.

Folgende Änderungen wurden in der Partitur der Gesamtausgabe vorgenommen:

Allgemeines

(1) Das Cembalo*, in Haydns Partitur nicht gesondert angeführt, war im 18. Jahrhundert eine Selbstverständlichkeit und eine Aufführung des Werkes ohne dieses Instrument ist undenkbar. Besonders im ersten Satz (T.39ff) erfüllt das Cembalo eine notwendige harmonische und klangliche Aufgabe.

(2) Das Fagott, ebenfalls nicht gesondert von Haydn angeführt, gehört zur Generalbasspraxis des 18. Jahrhunderts. Eine Untersuchung von den frühen Symphonien Haydns ergibt, dass auch er das Fagott als selbstverständlichen Teil des Basso Continuo voraussetzt, da er in vielen Werken plötzlich im System der Bassstimme " Fagotto Solo " notiert, ohne jedoch dieses Instrument zu Beginn des entsprechenden Satzes anzuführen. Derartige Stellen sind

---

* The work is wrongly placed in the chronological list. The subsequent discovery of the autograph, after Mandyczewski had completed his list of the 104 symphonies, showed that No. 49 should be placed after No. 35 (Dec. 1, 1767).

*Dieses Werk ist in der chronologischen Liste falsch eingeordnet. Das nach der Vollendung der von Mandyczewski entdeckte Autograph zeigt, dass Symphonie No. 49 No. 35 folgen sollte (1. Dezember 1767).

State Library). I have, therefore, suggested where the bassoon should play by placing the words " Senza Fag." or " Con Fag." in brackets throughout the symphony. In performances with large forces, it is perhaps advisable to use two bassoons, one doubling the bass part throughout, and one playing only in the fortes.

(3) Staccato dots. Haydn's autograph shows that the staccato marks were not only indications for staccato but also a kind of accent, for they are always written as long vertical dashes rather than mere dots. These have been engraved as small wedges except in passages where it is obvious that only dots are intended.

(4) Dynamic marks. Those added from secondary sources (i.e. not in the autograph) have been placed in normal brackets, whereas those added by me have been made recognizable by smaller print. Occasional ties missing in all the sources have been added in the form of dotted lines.

1st Movement

5: vln. II phrased in almost all the sources (incl. autograph) .

This was changed on basis of 1st vln.

35: forte on basis secondary sources (incl. Source B): compare bar 80.

61: vln. I ornament to be executed

78: vla., bass have crotchet with staccato instead of quaver.

90: A lacks ff.

2nd Movement

37: vla. in A—stave empty; supplied from B-E.

49: ob. II in all sources crotchet.

unter anderen in Symphonie Nr. 40 (Autograph im Brit. Museum), in Nr. 42 (Autograph im Esterházy-Archiv), in Nr. 45 (Autograph im Esterházy-Archiv) und in Nr. 55 (Autograph in der Berliner Staatsbibliothek) zu finden. Meine Vorschläge, an welchen Stellen das Fagott zu spielen sei, sind durch die eingeklammerten Worte " Senza Fag." oder " Con Fag." ersichtlich. In Aufführungen mit grosser Besetzung ist es vielleicht ratsam, zwei Fagotte zu beschäftigen, deren eines die Bassstimme durchwegs verdoppeln soll, während das andere nur in den Forte-Stellen herangezogen wird.

(3) Keile: Aus Haydns Autograph ist ersichtlich, dass das Staccato-Zeichen, das zumeist eher mit einem langen vertikalen Strich als mit Punkt notiert ist, nicht unbedingt als ein gewöhnliches Staccato aufzufassen sei, sondern zuweilen als eine Art von Akzent. Ausser den Stellen, in denen eindeutig Punkte (Staccato) beabsichtigt sind, wurden kleine Keile gestochen.

(4) Dynamik. Die aus sekundären Quellen entnommene (also nicht im Autograph enthaltene) Dynamik wurde in Klammern gesetzt, während die vom Herausgeber hinzugefügte durch kleineren Stich erkenntlich ist. Einige wenige, in allen Quellen fehlende, Bindebogen wurden in Form von punktierten Linien ergänzt.

1. Satz

5: Vln. II in fast allen Quellen (einschl. Autograph) . phrasiert; entsprechend Vln. I geändert.

35: forte auf Grund der sekundären Quellen (einschl. Quelle B); vgl. T. 80.

61: Die Verzierung der Vln. I muss folgendermassen ausgeführt werden:

3rd Movement

The phrasing of the quavers, as in

bars 3, 5 unclear; partly ♪♪♪♪

(convincing) and partly with a single slur (probably an abbreviation). The version of the G.A. retained. The same difficulty in the trio, bars 55, etc.

4th Movement

Parts have **C** instead of **¢** .

65: forte from secondary sources (an oversight in A ?).

122/3, 124/5: ob. slurs on basis parallel 46/7 and 48/9.

H. C. ROBBINS LANDON

78: Vla., Bass Vîertel mit Staccato an Stelle des Achtel.

90: A fehlt ff.

2. Satz

37: Vla. in A leeres System; nach B-E ergänzt.

49: Ob. II in allen Quellen Viertelnote.

3. Satz

Die Phrasierung der Achtelnoten ist, wie etwa in T. 3, 5, unklar; teils

♪♪♪♪ (überzeugend), teils

unter einem Bogen (wahrscheinlich eine Abkürzung). Die Version der Gesamtausgabe wurde beibehalten. Die gleiche Schwierigkeit besteht im Trio, T. 55, etc.

4. Satz

Die Stimmen notieren **C** anstatt **¢**

65: forte nach den sekundären Quellen (Versehen von A ?).

122/3, 124/5: Ob. Bogen auf Grund der Parallelstelle T. 46/7 und 48/9.

H. C. ROBBINS LANDON

Sinfonia No. 49
(La Passione)

Joseph Haydn
(1732-1809)

I

E. E. 6061

Ernst Eulenburg Ltd

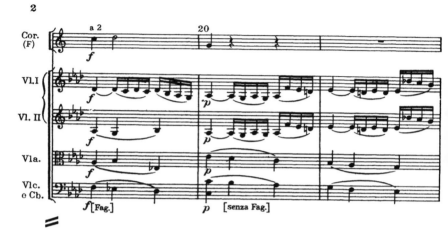

E.E. 6061

4

8

E. E. 6061

II

10

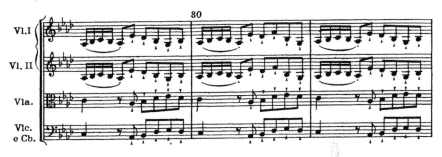

E. E. 6061

18

E. E. 6061

III

Menuet

24

Menuet da Cap

IV

Finale

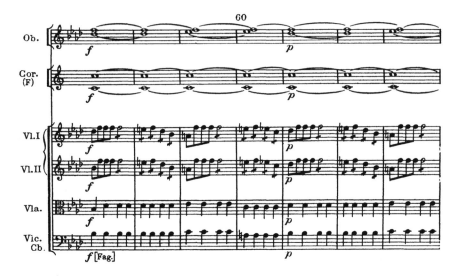

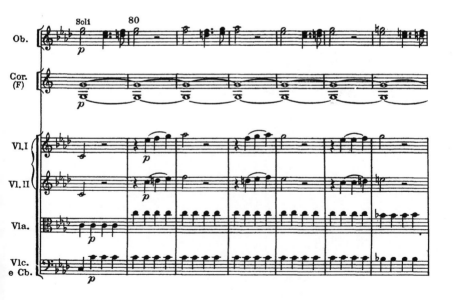

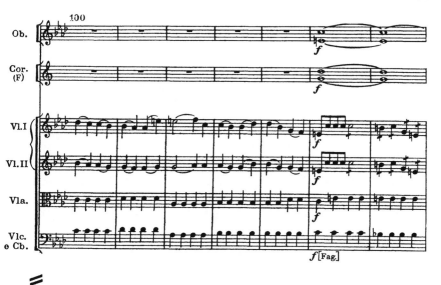

Finis Laus Deo.